Ma mère l'Oye

Mother Goose Suite

for one piano, four hands

by Maurice Ravel

edited by Weekley and Arganbright

kjos Neil A Kjos Music Company • San Diego, California

Translations
by John Magerus, Ph.D

I.
Pavane de la Belle au bois dormant

Pavane of the Sleeping Beauty in the Forest

II.
Petit Poucet

Il croyait trouver aisément son chemin par le moyen de son pain qu'il avait semé partout où il avait passé; mais il fut bien surpris lorsqu'il n'en put retrouver une seule miette: les oiseaux étaient venus qui avaient tout mangé.

Tom Thumb

He thought he would easily find his way by following the bread he had scattered everywhere he had gone, but he was very surprised when he couldn't find one single crumb; the birds had come and had eaten them all.

III.
Laideronnette, Impératrice des Pagodes

Elle se déshabilla et se mit dans le bain. Aussitôt pagodes et pagodines se mirent à chanter et à jouer des instruments: tels avaient des théorbes faits d'une coquille de noix; tels avaient des violes faites d'une coquille d'amande; car il fallait bien proportionner les instruments à leur taille.

Little Plain Jane, Empress of the Chinese Nodding-Dolls

She undressed and slipped into the bath. Immediately her Chinese nodding-dolls began to sing and to play miniature instruments: some had lutes made from walnuts while others had viols made from almond shells.

IV.
Les entretiens de la Belle et de la Bête

Belle: "Quand je pense à votre bon coeur, vous ne me paraissez pas si laid."
Bête: "Oh! dame oui! j'ai le coeur bon, mais je suis un monstre."
Belle: "Il y a bien des hommes qui sont plus monstres que vous."
Bête: "Si j'avais de l'esprit, je vous ferais un grand compliment pour vous remercier, mais je ne suis qu'une bête. La Belle, voulez-vous être ma femme?"
Belle: "Non, la Bête!"
Bête: "Je meurs content puisque j'ai le plaisir de vous revoir encore une fois."
Belle: "Non, ma chère Bête, vous ne mourrez pas: vous vivrez pour devenir mon époux!"

La Bête avait disparu et elle ne vit plus à ses pieds qu'un prince plus beau que l'Amour qui la remerciait d'avoir fini son enchantement.

Conversations of Beauty and the Beast

Beauty: "When I think about your kind heart, you don't seem so ugly to me."
Beast: "Oh yes, yes of course! I have a kind heart, but I am a monster!"
Beauty: "There are many men that are more monstrous than you."
Beast: "If I were clever, I would come up with a noble compliment to show you my thanks, but I'm only a beast. Beauty, do you want to be my wife?"
Beauty: "No, Beast."
Beast: "I can die happy now, since I have the pleasure of seeing you once again."
Beauty: "No, my dear Beast, you will not die; you will live so you can become my husband."

The Beast disappeared and she saw at her feet a prince, more handsome than the god of love himself, who thanked her for having brought his enchantment to an end.

V.
Le jardin féerique

The Enchanted Garden

ISBN 0-8497-5252-3

About the editors

Dallas Weekley and Nancy Arganbright Weekley have brought a great degree of public understanding and appreciation to the four-hand literature through their performances in the United States and Europe, and from their teaching base at the University of Wisconsin in La Crosse. Weekley and Arganbright's editions make it possible for pianists to enjoy their experience, research, and love of the literature.

"Weekley and Arganbright ably and winningly demonstrated that the piano duet is a successful medium for the widest range of musical expression. Though limiting their repertoire to orignal works for four hands at one piano, their program affords both variety and substance in works ranging from the classic to the contemporary era."

London Times

Weekley and Arganbright Editions

Ma mère l'Oye   *WP138*
Pachelbel's Canon in D   *WP1047*
Rossini's William Tell Overture arr. by Gottschalk   *WP119*
Schubert's German Dances and Ecossaises, opus 33   *WP97*
Three Baroque Pieces   *WP127*
Twice as Nice (Original Duets for 1 piano, 4 hands), Volume 1   *WP57*
Twice as Nice, Volume 2   *WP58*
Twice as Nice, Volume 3   *WP79*

About the composer and music

Maurice Ravel (1875-1937) loved small children and sometimes would disappear from an adult gathering to visit the nursery, playing children's games. He wrote *Ma mère l'Oye* (Mother Goose) in 1908 as a gift for two young friends, Jean and Mimi Godebski. The various scenes were inspired mostly by stories of Charles Perrault, but also by Spanish and oriental tales of the Comtesse d'Aulnoy and Marie Leprince de Beaumont. The composer wrote: "The idea of conjuring up the poetry of childhood in these pieces led me to simplify my style and clarify my writing." The result is remarkably lyrical, picturesque, and appealing.

The suite was originally written between 1908 and 1910 for piano duet. Ravel later scored it for orchestra, adding a prelude and four long interludes. It was performed as a children's ballet in Paris in 1912.

I.
Pavane de la Belle au bois dormant
Pavane of the Sleeping Beauty in the Forest

WP138

II.
Petit Poucet
Tom Thumb

He thought he would easily find his way by following the bread he had scattered everywhere he had gone, but he was very surprised when he couldn't find one single crumb; the birds had come and had eaten them all.

Note: ⌞⌟ and ⌐⌐ are alternate hand indications.

la m. g. expressif
(expressive left hand)

III.
Laideronnette, Impératrice des Pagodes

Little Plain Jane, Empress of the Chinese Nodding-Dolls*

She undressed and slipped into the bath. Immediately her Chinese nodding-dolls began to sing and to play miniature instruments: some had lutes made from walnuts while others had viols made from almond shells.

*Nodding-dolls are porcelain figurines with moveable heads.

a) May be taken with R.H.

b) Final C# may be taken with L.H., but without accent.

c) Not in first edition; Ravel was reported to have
included these gong effects in his own performances.

18

WP138

a) May be taken with R.H.

22

WP138

b) Final C# may be taken with L.H., but without accent.

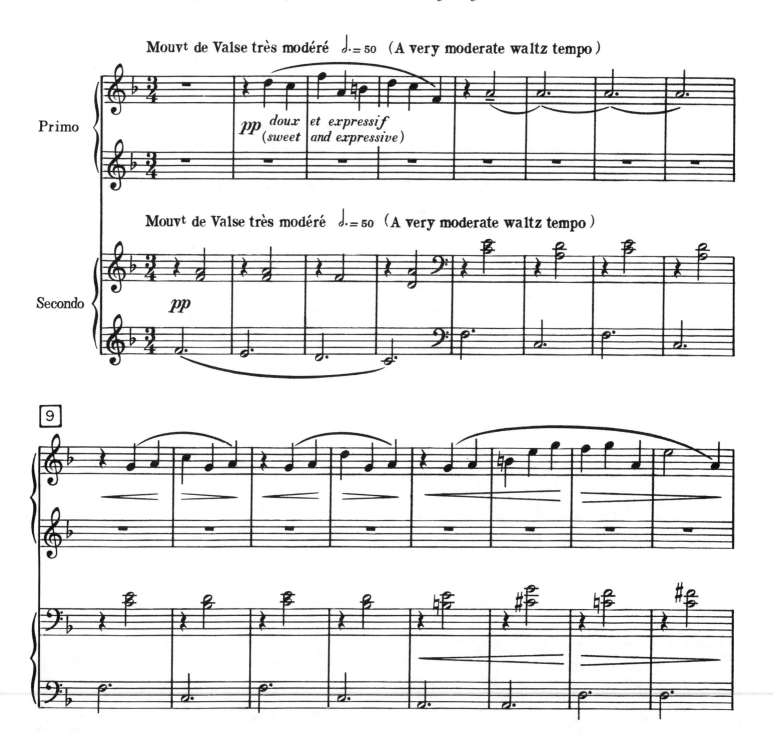

IV.
Les entretiens de la Belle et la Bête
Conversations of Beauty and the Beast

Beauty: "When I think about your kind heart, you don't seem so ugly to me."

Beast: "Oh yes, yes of course! I have a kind heart, but I am a monster!"

Beauty: "There are many men who are more monstrous than you."

Beast: "If I were clever, I would come up with a noble compliment to show you my thanks, but I'm only a beast. Beauty, do you want to be my wife?"

Beauty: "No, Beast."

Beast: "I can die happy now, since I have the pleasure of seeing you once again."

Beauty: "No, my dear Beast, you will not die; you will live so you can become my husband."

The Beast disappeared and she saw at her feet a prince, more handsome than the god of love himself, who thanked her for having brought his enchantment to an end.

V.
Le jardin féerique
The Enchanted Garden

un peu en dehors (*a little emphasis*)

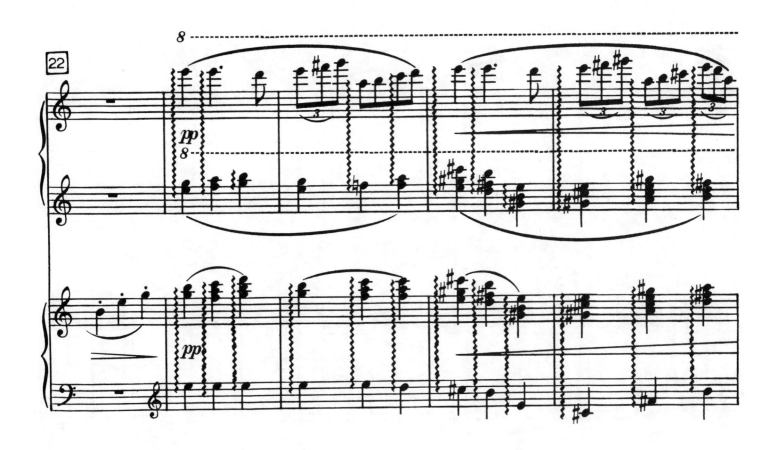

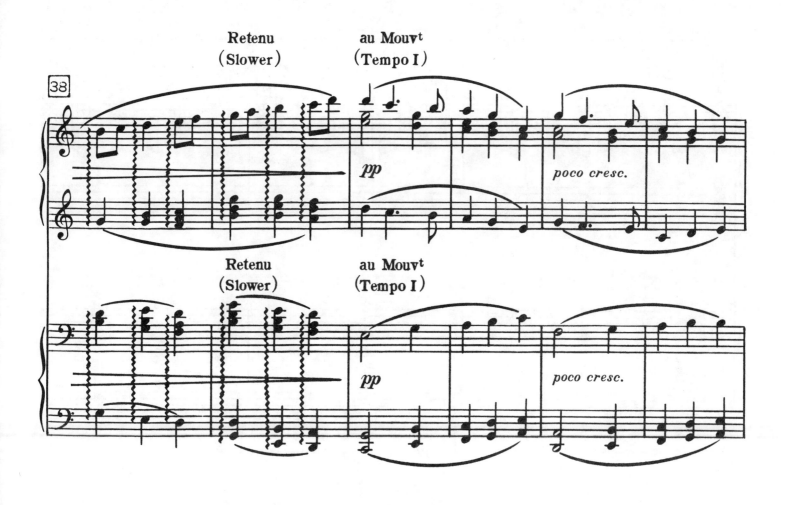

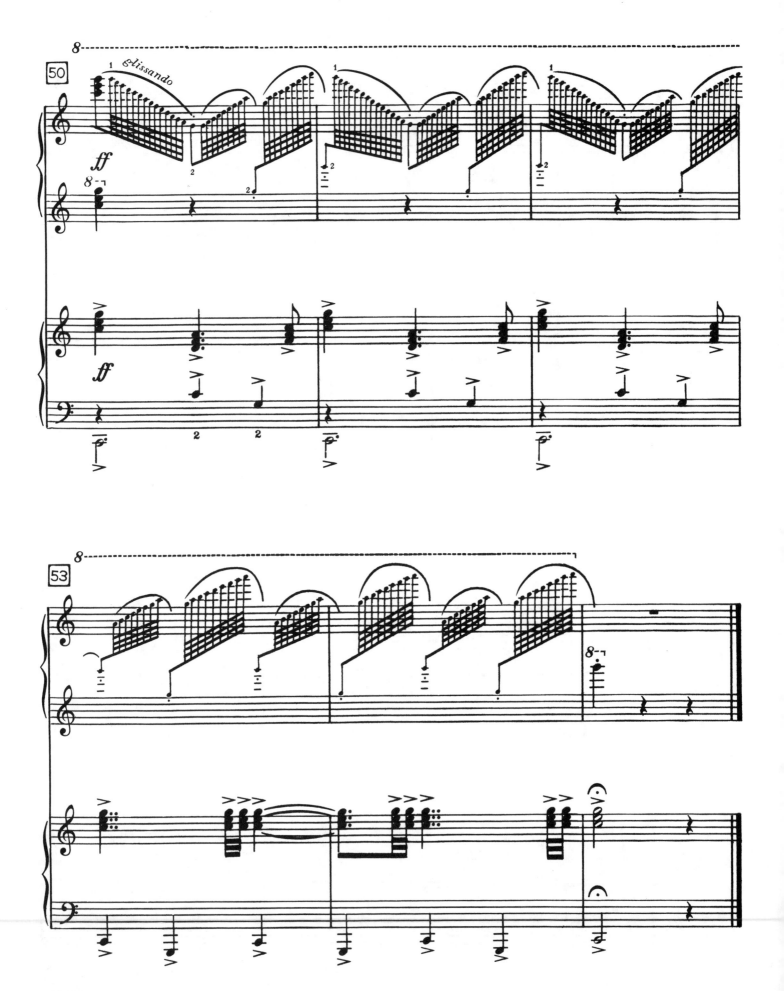

WEEKLEY & ARGANBRIGHT EDITIONS

Elementary Duet Collections

Easy For Two – Preparatory Level (WP530)
Four American Folk Songs (WP159)✳
Piano Together – Level 1 (WP531)
Primo Light (WP151)
Primo Profiles (WP338)
Secondo Light (WP345)
Twelve Classic Duets (WP395)

Intermediate Duet Collections

Christmas Liszt For Two (WP329)
Classics For Two (WP308)✳
Czerny's Sonatina, Op. 156 No. 2 (WP189)
Five Joplin Rags (WP178)✳
Four Joplin Waltzes (WP316)✳
Hymns For Two (WP313)
Kuhlau's Sonatina Opus 17 (WP160)✳
Pachelbel's Canon in D (WP1047)
Romantic Piano Duets (WP193)✳
Rossini's William Tell Overture (WP119)✳
Schubert's German Dances and Ecossaises (WP97)
Summer Dreams (WP364)✳
Three Baroque Pieces (WP127)✳
Three Sonatinas (WP340)
Twice As Nice, Vol. 1 (WP57)✳
Twice As Nice, Vol. 2 (WP58)
Twice As Nice, Vol. 3 (WP79)✳

Graded Duet Collections from the Neil A. Kjos Piano Library

Easy For Two – Preparatory Level (WP530)
Piano Together – Level 1 (WP531)
Brahms Waltzes Op. 39 – Level 7 (WP537)
Duet Repertoire – Level 8 (WP538) fall 1999
Duet Repertoire – Level 9 (WP539)✳
Franz Schubert Selected Works – Level 10 (WP565)

Late Intermediate - Advanced Duet Collections

Brahms Waltzes Op. 39 – Level 7 (WP537)
Duet Repertoire – Level 8 (WP538) fall 1999
Duet Repertoire – Level 9 (WP539)✳
Ma Mère L'Oye (Mother Goose) – Ravel (WP138)✳
Mephisto Waltz – Liszt (WP348)
Petite Suite – Debussy (WP327)✳
Poulenc Sonata (WP566) fall 1999
Franz Schubert Selected Works – Level 10 (WP565)

References and Texts

Piano Duet, The - A Learning Guide (WP381)
Schubert's Music For Piano Four Hands (WA1)

✳ Indicates a National Federation of Music Clubs Festival Selection